The Geology of Pembrokeshire

DR. BRIAN S. JOHN

GW00656545

Abercastle Publications

CONTENTS

FOREWORD

This book has been written for those who, like myself, have had no formal training in geology. I hope that it will be of interest to some of those who tramp the footpaths and lanes of our beautiful county: local people on weekend walks and drives, teachers and schoolchildren, holiday makers, and students involved in field excursions and project work.

In the text which follows I have tried to simplify the complicated geology of Pembrokeshire as far as possible, and yet I have endeavoured to be accurate. Grid references are given for the most important sites, to aid visitors to the county who may be unfamiliar with many of the local placenames. Appendix I lists, for convenience, some of the more interesting geological localities of the county, together with brief notes on the rocks to be seen at each site. Since many readers will feel uncomfortable in the company of the geological terms used in the text, a brief glossary (Appendix II) has been added. And on the last few pages there is a list of references which might prove useful to those who would like to undertake further geological study. Some of these references are also referred to in the text. I hope that these assorted "extras" will make the book valuable not only to the armchair geologist but also to the intrepid field explorer.

For those who wish to be well equipped for more advanced studies in the field, it is a good idea to purchase the following:

The *"South Wales" Regional Geology Handbook,* by T. N. George;

The simplified *Geological Map of Pembrokeshire,* available from National Park Information Centres;

A copy of the local *Tide Tables,* if you intend to look at the coastal cliffs (abbreviated in the Coast Path booklets in this series);

The official *1" Geological Survey Maps* of Pembrokeshire,

namely: No. 227 Milford, No. 228 Haverfordwest, No. 245 Pembroke.

If you intend to look at rock exposures in inaccesible places, use a pair of binoculars rather then a climbing rope. You do **not** need a geological hammer in the field; it may be a fine status symbol, but in the process of rock-bashing you will probably hurt yourself and certainly damage the environment. Please remember that many geological sites in the county are of immense value; rock outcrops may seem indestructible, but they are just as easily destroyed as hedgerows full of shrubs and flowers. So enjoy the rocks of Pembrokeshire by all means, but leave them where they are for those who come after you.

Finally, please remember that while most of the sites described on the following pages are close to the Coastal Footpath, many are either on private property or can be reached only by crossing private property. Please respect the Country Code at all times, and ask permission to visit any sites where access is not clearly marked.

INTRODUCTION

The rocks of Pembrokeshire have excited the attention of geologists for many years. Around the magnificent cliffed coasts of the National Park there are exposures of immensely old rocks, and many complicated structures can be examined in detail. Most of the rocks of which the county is composed are more than 280 million years old and the more recent rocks so typical of South-East England are not represented here at all.

Perhaps the most striking feature of the local geology is the amazing variety of rock-types compressed into one small area. In contrast, as one travels eastwards or north-eastwards in Wales the main rock outcrops separate and become broader, so that the geology becomes less complicated and, on the whole, less interesting. The reason for the compression of so many rock types into this south-west corner of Wales lies in the great mountain building periods referred to as the "Caledonian Orogeny" (about 400 million years ago) and the "Armorican Orogeny" (about 290 million years ago). The mountain range which was constructed during the former period had a general trend from E.N.E. towards W.S.W., whereas the later Armorican mountains trended E.S.E. to W.N.W. In Pembrokeshire the worn-down roots of these ancient mountain systems are in particularly close contact (Fig. 1).

As one would expect from this structural pattern, most of the older rocks are to be found in the north of the county and the younger rocks in the south. While there are some exceptions to this rule, we may generalise and say that a line drawn from near Druidston on St. Bride's Bay eastwards through Haverfordwest and thence to the county boundary at Tavernspite separates two distinct geological "provinces" or regions. To the north of this line most of the rocks are of Pre-Cambrian and Lower Palaeozoic age (that is, more than 395 million years old), whereas to the south most of the rocks are of Upper Palaeozoic age (that is, less than 395 million years old but more than 225 million years old). For convenience we will refer to these regions later as the "Northern Province" and the "Southern Province".

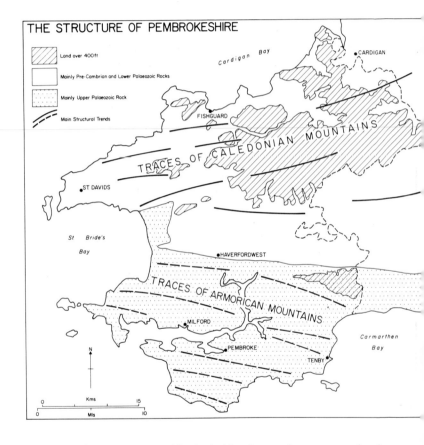

Figure 1: The structure of Pembrokeshire, showing the two structural regions.

FUNDAMENTALS

Rock Types

Befre looking at the rocks of Pembrokeshire in more detail, it is worth mentioning the main rock types that we can examine in the field (Fig. 2).

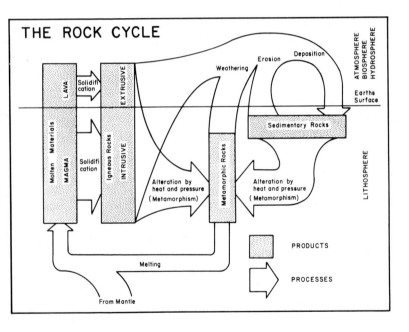

Figure 2: The 'rock 'cycle'', illustrating the relationships between the main rock types. (Based upon a diagram in *"Major Features of the Earth's Surface"*. Open University Science Foundation Course Unit 24).

1.   **Sedimentary** rocks are the most widespread of all, having been laid down over long periods of time as sediments, whether in rivers, the sea or lakes, or on the land surface. Examples are mudstones, laid down in deep standing water; limestone, formed through the slow accumulation of organic calcium carbonate; and coal, derived from decayed sub-tropical vegetation. Hence sedimentary rocks may be formed from mineral fragments, or from organic debris, or from a mixture of both. They are generally layered or bedded, and are transformed from loose sediments to solid rock by the pressure of overlying sediments as they accumulate.

2.   **Igneous** rocks are the basic earth materials, which find their way from the interior to the earth's outer crust largely by means of volcanic activity. Those igneous rocks which reach the surface and solidify there are called **volcanic** or **extrusive**; but igneous rocks which solidify at depth, possibly disturbing or replacing older rocks, are termed **intrusive** (Fig. 2). Among the extrusive rocks are lavas, tuffs and ashes, while the intrusive group includes granite, gabbro and dolerite. In Pembrokeshire many of the prominent hill masses coincide with the outcrops of igneous rock, for they have been more resistant to erosion than the layered sedimentary rocks. The surface distribution of igneous rocks is rather unpredictable, and their outcrops are generally irregular in outline.

3.   **Metamorphic** rocks are greatly altered by heat or pressure so that they acquire characteristics different from the parent rock (Fig. 2). They may form around the margins of igneous intrusions, or beneath a great thickness of overlying sediments, or in zones subject to shattering or deformation as a result of mountain-building processes. Examples of metamorphic rocks are marble (formed from limestone), slate (formed from shale or mudstone) and gneiss (sometimes formed from siltstone or fine sandstone). Metamorphic rocks are not as common in Pembrokeshire as either of the other major rock groups.

Stratigraphy

Each rock type, when encountered and identified in the field, can tell us a great deal about the climatic and other environmental conditions which prevailed when it was formed.

While the layman may have neither the experience nor the proper equipment for the study of mineralogy, petrology or palaeontology, he can still obtain much pleasure from observing the physical characteristics of rocks and noting how individual rock types are distributed in space and time. The analysis of rock distributions enables many types of geological study to be placed into a historical framework; it enables us to recognize the inter-relationships between rock characteristics, the processes responsible, and the creatures which were alive at the time.

In particular, it is the succession of the layers, or **strata**, of sedimentary rocks which gives a natural chronological table into which all the events of geological time can be fitted. By the straightforward application of a number of simple laws (Middlemiss, 1969) geologists have been able, over the past 200 years or so, to construct an accurate timetable of geological events. Some of the laws are shown diagrammatically on Figure 3, and can be summarised as follows:

(a) According to the **law of superposition**, each rock layer within a sedimentary sequence is younger than the one beneath. Rock layers are said to be conformable when they have been deposited without interruption, but where there are "unconformities" or where strata have been tilted or even overturned this law must be applied only with the greatest caution.

(b) The **law of contained fragments** states that if eroded fragments of one rock are contained in another (for example in a conglomerate), then the rock containing the fragments is the younger of the two.

(c) The **law of intrusive junctions** states that if an igneous rock has been intruded into a sedimentary layer, or into another igneous rock, then the intruded rock must be the younger.

9

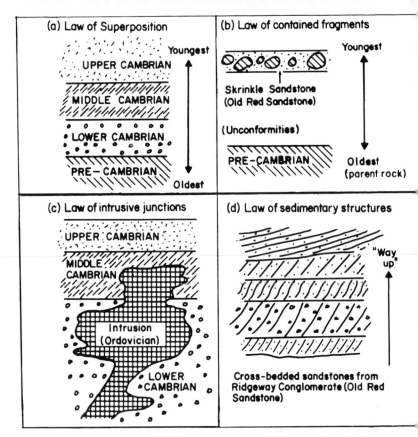

Figure 3: Illustrations of the four simple stratigraphic laws mentioned in the text. The diagrams represent actual situations in the geology of Pembrokeshire.

(d) According to the **law of sedimentary structures** it is generally possible to recognise the "way up" of a stratum by comparing it with situations which we may recognise in present-day sedimentary environments. Thus we may use Sir Charles Lyell's famous "Principle of Uniformitarianism", summarised in the saying "The present is the key to the past".

There are many other rules which geologists use in the interpretation of rock sequences, and these will be found by referring to the standard geology texts listed at the end of the book. For the situation in Pembrokeshire, Figure 3 demonstrates simply the way in which the four laws quoted above can be employed in the field as an aid to understanding.

A simplified stratigraphic column for Pembrokeshire is given on Table 1. Note from the table that the main geological **eras** and **periods** can be recognised on a world scale, and are time units; on the other hand the sequence of **formations** and **series** is unique to this part of Wales, and is referred to by means of stratigraphic units.

Fossils

In situations where it is difficult to match rocks by their physical appearance alone, fossils can provide many valuable clues. The Cambrian rocks of Pembrokeshire contain fossils which represent the earliest forms of marine life. The fossils include sponges, marine molluscs and trilobites. The succeeding Ordovician and Silurian rocks, which look similar to some Cambrian rocks, are rich in fossils from more advanced forms of life, particularly graptolites. Corals and molluscs are common in Silurian rocks, and in later rock series fish and land plants appear. There are of course innumerable corals and other animal remains in the Carboniferous Limestone, while the Coal Measures preserve abundant plant fossils. Those fossils which are most important for dating purposes are referred to as **index fossils**.

The Making of Mountains

The mountain-building periods referred to in the Introduction (p. 3) and on the stratigraphic column (Table 1) were responsible for the tilting, folding and shattering of many of the local rocks. Mountain-building phases are now known to be associated with the slow collisions between rigid crustal plates which are "afloat" on the earth's semi-fluid mantle. The dimensions and characteristics of individual mountain chains vary according to

11

Era			Age in millions of years	Period (and cycles of earth movement)	Formation
Cenozoic	Quaternary			Holocene	Recent
				Pleistocene	Glacial
			— 2 —		
	Tertiary			Pliocene Miocene ALPINE OROGENY Oligocene Eocene Palaeocene	
			— 65 —		
Mesozoic				Cretaceous Jurassic Rhaetic Triassic	
Palaeozoic	Upper Palaeozoic		280	Permian	
				ARMORICAN OROGENY Carboniferous	Coal Measures (Westphalian) Millstone Grit (Namurian) Carboniferous Limestone
			345		
				Devonian and Old Red Sandstone	Upper Old Red Sandstone Middle Old Red Sandstone Lower Old Red Sandstone
			···· 395 ····		
	Lower Palaeozoic			CALEDONIAN OROGENY Silurian	Ludlow Wenlock Upper Llandovery Lower Llandovery
			440		
				Ordovician	Bala Llandilo Llanvirn Arenig
			500		
				Cambrian	Upper Middle Lower
			— 570 —		
Eozoic			3000	CHARNIAN. OROGENY Pre-Cambrian	Dimetian Pebidian Johnston

Table1: A simplified stratigraphic column for Pembrokeshire, showing the main eras, periods and local rock formations.

12

the nature of the colliding plates (that is, whether they are "oceanic" or "continental" plates) and according to their speed and directions of movement. Since these ideas on continental drift and "plate tectonics" are now accepted by most geologists (Calder, 1972), it is wise to use them in our interpretations of the major mountain-building periods of the British Isles.

The Pre-Cambrian rocks of Pembrokeshire have probably been deformed during at least one (but more likely several) collisions between plates in the immensely long period between 4,000 million years ago and 570 million years ago. The Caledonian Orogeny, which was responsible for the folding and faulting of the older rocks of the county, resulted from the compression of an ancient geosyncline about 400 million years ago as the two ancient continents of North America and Europe collided.

On the southern side of the Caledonian Mountains the Old Red Sandstone and Carboniferous rocks were deposited, until about 290 million years ago the African plate trundled up from the south. In the resulting collision the Armorican mountains were formed and the mighty "supercontinent" of Pangaea was born. At this time all of the continents of the world were locked together in a single huge land-mass. Whatever rocks may have been laid down in Pembrokeshire since then have subsequently been removed during over 225 million years or erosion, while sea-level has risen and fallen and Pangaea has split up into the continents as we know them today (Calder, 1972).

The mountain-building phase which created the Alps, less than 65 million years ago, resulted from a series of complicated movements of plates around the Mediterranean; the only effects in Pembrokeshire were slight faulting and bending of rocks which were already extremely distorted by the upheavals of the past.

Thus we can see that the geology of Pembrokeshire's small land area holds a fascinating and unique record of earth history. The **rocks** themselves contain the details of changes in the environment over much of geological time; these changes can be discovered from a study of both the physical character of the rocks and the fossils they contain. And in the **structures** displayed in the spectacular cliffs around the coasts of the county can be seen the records of crustal movements, on an almost unimaginable scale, which have shaped and reshaped the face of the earth.

With these thoughts in our minds, we shall go on to examine some of the characteristics of the rocks to be found in the Northern and Southern geological provinces of Pembrokeshire.

NORTHERN GEOLOGICAL PROVINCE

As noted above, most of the ancient rocks of Pembrokeshire are to be found to the north of a line between Druidston and Tavernspite (Fig. 1). The generalised geological map of the area (Fig. 4) shows that the most widespread rock outcrops are of Ordovician sedimentary rocks, but there are many other rock-types to be found, especially in the western part of the province. A glance at Table 1 will show something of the wide variety of sedimentary and igneous rocks which may be encountered, in the beautiful cliffs of the St David's peninsula in particular.

The structure of north Pembrokeshire (Fig. 1) reflects the events of the Caledonian mountain-building phase, when pressure was exerted from both north-west and south-east by colliding continents. The ancient rocks were buckled into a series of troughs (synclines) and ridges (anticlines), some of which can be traced north-eastwards into Cardiganshire and Central Wales.

One of the most important anticlines is called the Teifi Anticline, which seems to extend all the way westwards to the coast of St Bride's Bay; here, at its western end, it is called the Haycastle Anticline, which coincides with the outcrop of Pre-Cambrian igneous rocks (Fig. 4) between Treffgarne and the sea at Newgale.

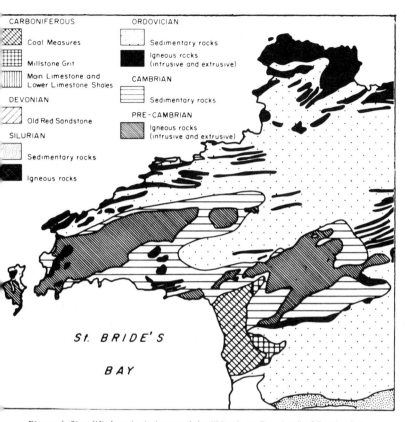

ORDOVICIAN

Coal Measures

Sedimentary rocks

Igneous rocks
(intrusive and extrusive)

Millstone Grit

CAMBRIAN

Main Limestone and
Lower Limestone Shales

Sedimentary rocks

DEVONIAN

PRE-CAMBRIAN

Old Red Sandstone

Igneous rocks
(intrusive and extrusive)

SILURIAN

Sedimentary rocks

Igneous rocks

S†. BRIDE'S

BAY

Figure 4: Simplified geological map of the "Northern Province" of Pembrokeshire.

Another important anticline is the St David's Anticline, which is responsible for the exposure of the strip of old rocks along the axis of St David's Peninsula. If one looks at the topographic maps of Pembrokeshire, one can see that the "grain" of the country, especially in the uplands, coincides with the Caledonian trend. Hence the main mountain ridges, such as the rocky moorlands of Mynydd Preselau and Mynydd Carningli, run parallel with the Caledonian structures, and it is clear that the low, gently undulating St David's Peninsula itself is a worn-down remnant of the Caledonian mountain range (Fig. 1). The beautiful, bleak Treffgarne Ridge (910233), running S.W.-N.E. from Roch to the Treffgarne Gorge, is another Caledonian structure. If we look at the geological map of north Pembrokeshire on Figure 4, we can see how the abundant "sills" of Ordovician igneous rock also bring out the Caledonian trend, especially in the Preselau uplands. Further west the spectacular rocky ridges of Carnllidi (738280), Carn Treliwyd and Penberry (near St David's) coincide with outcrops of Ordovician igneous rock, and the same may be said of the Garn-fawr ridge (Pen Caer) which reaches a summit altitude of 699 feet above sea-level. Each of these follows the important Caledonian trend.

Where the Caledonian earth-movements have exerted especially great pressures upon the Pre-Cambrian and Lower Palaeozoic rocks of north Pembrokeshire, they have often been forced to give way by fracturing or shearing. Thus we can recognise abundant **faults** which may have brought rocks of widely differing textures and ages adjacent to one another. These can be seen in many cliff exposures, but they are generally difficult to trace inland, where they may run for five miles or more. For example, there are long faults bounding the outcrops of Pre-Cambrian rocks between the Daugleddau and Walwyns Castle (Figure 4), and there is an important fault between the Coal Measures and the Cambrian rocks at the northern end of Newgale beach (847224). There are many faults exposed around the coast of Pen Caer, and almost all of the rock contacts to be seen along the beach at Whitesand Bay (733270) are faulted. The inner part of the sheltered Solva Harbour has been eroded along a faulted zone which cuts across both Cambrian and Ordovician rocks. So common are these faulted contacts throughout the Pre-Cambrian and Lower Palaeozoic rocks of Pembrokeshire that they may be found almost everywhere; only very rarely can one examine a cliff section without seeing evidence of faulting, often with shattering of the adjacent strata.

16

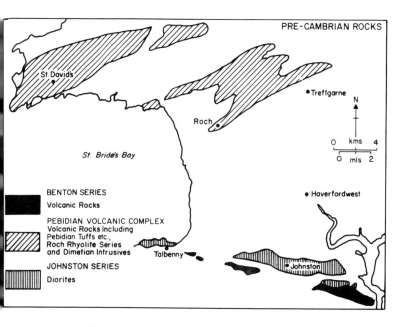

PRE-CAMBRIAN ROCKS

St. David's

Treffgarne

Roch

N

kms   4

mls   2

St. Bride's Bay

BENTON SERIES
Volcanic Rocks

Haverfordwest

PEBIDIAN VOLCANIC COMPLEX
Volcanic Rocks Including
Pebidian Tuffs etc.,
Roch Rhyolite Series
and Dimetian Intrusives

Talbenny

Johnston

JOHNSTON SERIES
Diorites

Figure 5: Areas of Pre-Cambrian rock exposures.

The ancient rocks of St David's Peninsula and the Roch-Treffgarne area

In this area, long famous among geologists, there is an enormous variety of rock types, brought into close contact with one another by the very complicated structures of Caledonian age. The oldest rocks of the area are the Pre-Cambrian "Pebidian" rocks, probably around 1,000 million years old and exposed in a belt along the centre of the St David's Anticline for a distance of about 8 miles from Ramsey Sound (Fig. 5). Among the Pebidian rocks are tuffs, greenish acid rocks, and agglomerates with occasional conglomerates and frequent interbedded lava flows. Some of these rocks can be seen on the coast between Porthlysgi (732236) and Ramsey Sound. In places there are intrusive rocks,

17

Figure 6: Sketch of Maiden Castle, one of the crags of Roch Rhyolite on the west side of Treffgarne Gorge.

such as granites and dolerites, interspersed with the volcanic rocks; these can be seen on the headland and islands just east of Porthlysgi, and there are other outcrops in small crags or knolls in Merry Vale (745250) and around St David's (Baker, 1971). One of the most unique and beautiful of the Pre-Cambrian rocks is the "halleflinta" exposed in St Non's Bay and in the Caerbwdi Valley below Pont Clegyr (769251); this is a fine-grained, almost glassy, blue-green rock which is translucent when broken into sharp splinters.

The intrusive rocks of this area were once thought to be younger than the Pebidian volcanic rocks, and were blessed with the distinguishing name "Dimetian". However, it is now thought that all of the Pre-Cambrian rocks of the St David's area are of approximately the same age, although the terms "Pebidian" and "Dimetian" are still used (Table 1).

18

In the extensive outcrop of Pre-Cambrian rocks around Hays-castle, Roch and Treffgarne, there are similar examples of Pebidian lava-flows, tuffs and ashes, but the structures here are very complex. The main area of intrusive rock is to the east of Hayscastle (897256), according to the work of Williams (1934). Running parallel with the Hayscastle Anticline is the Roch-Treff-garne Anticline, which exposes the rocks of the "Roch rhyolitic series". Included in this are volcanic breccias, ashes and ashy bedded flagstones, but the most resistant rock is the Roch rhyolite itself, a greenish blue fine-grained silicified rock which weathers almost white. It is exposed in the small crag at Roch Castle, at Plumstone Rock, and in the magnificent crage at Poll Carn (953245) and Maiden Castle (954248) above the Treffgarne Gorge (Fig. 6).

The later Cambrian rocks (which are less than 570 million years old) occur quite extensively around the flanks of the Pre-Cambrian outcrops (Fig. 4). However, there are very few natural exposures of these rocks inland, and most studies of the Cambrian have been made on the spectacular cliffed coast on the north shore of St Bride's Bay.

From Porth-clais (743240) to Solva Harbour (800240) succes-sively younger Cambrian rocks can be seen in the cliffs, and there are scattered occurrences of Cambrian rocks further east as far as Cwm-mawr (845229) and the north end of Newgale beach. Cambrian rocks can also be seen in the cliffs at Whitesand Bay (Fig. 7) and further south towards the coast of Ramsey Sound. All of the Cambrian rocks in Pembrokeshire are sedimentary in type; they accumulated in a deepening ocean basin, and hence they become generally finer upwards. They contain the first signs of life in the Pembrokeshire rock sequence, and through their fossils show the growth of communities of many different marine animals. The sedimentary rocks exposed on the plateau-like sur-face of the St David's Peninsula have given rise to thin, stony and sandy soils which were famous until the nineteenth century for their fine crops of barley and other cereals.

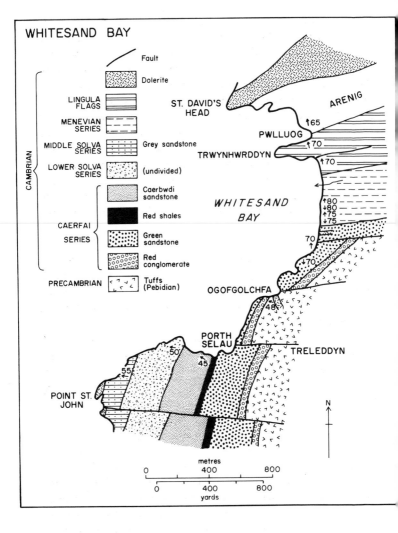

Figure 7: The Cambrian rocks exposed in the cliffs around Whitesand Bay. Note the inluence of faults running inland from the coast. Drawn from a map by Stead and Williams, 1971.

20

Steeply dipping Lower Cambrian rocks are particularly well exposed along parts of the cliffs between Porth-clais and Porth-y-Rhaw (787243). The oldest rock of the "Caerfai Series" is the basal red conglomerate, which has a very distinctive colour and which rests unconformably upon the local Pre-Cambrian rocks. Above this is a thick series of fine-grained green sandstones which grades upwards into a striking horizon of red shales. The red shales are generally less than 40 feet thick, but they are conspicuous in the cliffs at Caerfai (760244), at Castell on Ramsey Sound, and at Cwm-mawr. However, their geological importance lies not so much in their magnificent colour as in the fact that they are the lowest horizon in Pembrokeshire from which fossils have been obtained (George 1970). The upper part of the Lower Cambrian in this area consists of up to 500 feet of fine-grained green and purple "Caerbwdi Sandstone", which is again highly distinctive, being best exposed in Caerbwdi Bay (766244). This famous sandstone was used in the construction of St David's Cathedral.

At higher levels within the Cambrian sequence the rocks become gradually more difficult to recognise on the basis of colour. In the Lower and Middle Solva Series (exposed, for example, to the east of Caerbwdi Bay and on the sides of Solva Harbour) there are green pebbly sandstones and green or purple mudstones and sandstones, but above this the Middle and Upper Cambrian rocks are generally composed of dull grey, buff and brown fine sandstones, shales and mudstones. It is often difficult for the inexperienced eye to distinguish between these rocks and the various series of the Ordovician.

An excellent area for the study of these various Cambrian rocks is the coastal stretch between St Non's Bay (753244) and Caerbwdi Bay, centred on Caerfai (Fig. 8). In particular, the Caerbwdi Sandstone can be studied at beach level with the rocks of the Solva Series exposed on the headlands for those who wish to do a little low-tide scrambling.

21

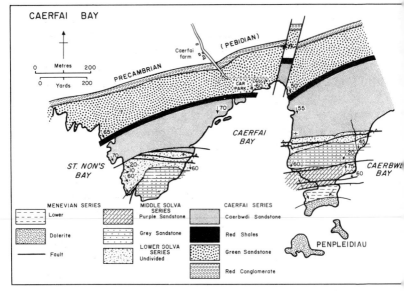

Figure 8: Cambrian rocks of the Caerfai and Solva series, particularly well exposed around Caerfai Bay. Drawn from a map by Stead and Williams, 1971.

Exposures of Ordovician rocks

The Ordovician rocks cover a huge area of north Pembrokeshire. Many of the mudstones and shales (locally termed "rab") encountered in small exposures in the upper basins of the Western Cleddau and Eastern Cleddau are of Ordovician age. So too, are the rocks of the Preselau Hills and the basin of the Afon Nyfer to the east (Fig. 4). Many stone walls and buildings in these parts of north Pembrokeshire are built of thick shale slabs, and thinner flagstones have often been used for roofing purposes. Most of the rocks were laid down in deep sea water, and because the sediments are difficult to classify on the basis of physical characteristics alone, the Ordovician system is divided largely on the basis of its contained fossil graptolites. The four main series which can be recognised in Pembrokeshire are shown in Table 1.

These are made up for the most part of shales, ashes, sandstones, mudstones and thin limestones. Many of these rocks are light in colour, but most fossil graptolites are to be found in dark grey or black carbonaceous shales interbedded with greywackes and probably deposited at great depths. In many areas (such as Rosebush and Efailwen) the rocks have been altered by heat and pressure to form slates, many of them excellent for roofing purposes.

During the Ordovician period there was violent volcanic activity, particularly in Arenig and Llanvirn times (see Table 1). Lavas of great thickness were poured out of local volcanoes, at first in submarine eruptions but later, as the cones grew and emerged from the sea, above sea-level (George, 1970). We can imagine that these volcanoes must have developed in the same way as Surtsey, which emerged from the sea off the coast of Iceland in 1963. Ashes and tuffs were laid down over wide areas, and here and there one can find sediments formed after the coastal erosion of the volcano flanks.

In addition to the extrusive rocks of Ordovician age, there are many intrusions throughout north Pembrokeshire (Fig. 4). These intruded igneous rocks (for example, dolerites and gabbros) are generally found in sills, which are today exposed as long narrow strips. But occasionally there seems to have been wholesale replacement of older rocks by Ordovician intrusions, not only in the area of Ordovician sediments but also among the Pre-Cambrian and Cambrian outcrops. In many parts of north Pembrokeshire stone walls are made of these hard, grey igneous rocks.

Among the best-known localities for Ordovician rocks is Abereiddy Bay (797313), which is eroded into soft Llanvirn and Llandeilo shales. Here, in one of the quarries, may be found the famous "tuning-fork graptolites".

Almost all of the bays and inlets on the coast between St David's Head and Strumble Head (893414) are cut into soft Ordovician shales, whereas most of the headlands coincide with more resistant Ordovician igneous rocks (George, 1970). For example, the bays of Pwllderi (893385) and Porth Maenmelyn on the west side of Pen Caer are cut into the so-called "tetrograptus shales", whereas the nearby headlands are of volcanic and intrusive rocks. In the north of Pen Caer there is a large area of pillow-lavas, rhyolites, agglomerates and ash beds; some of these rocks can be examined on a day-trip to the bleak surroundings of the Strumble Head lighthouse. Not far away, near the tip of Penanglas (948405) there are "columns" of dolerite reminiscent of the Giant's Causeway. On St David's Head there are fine exposures of gabbro, while there are dolerites at Penberry and in the stone quarry north-west of Porthgain (807327). The well-known Treffgarne "granite" quarry (958240) is not cut in granite at all, but in ashes, andesitic agglomerates and tuffs which are part of the Treffgarne Volcanic Series.

Perhaps the most famous of all the Ordovician igneous rocks of Pembrokeshire are the dolerites which outcrop at Carn Meini (143324) on the southern flank of Mynydd Preselau. Here, according to H. H. Thomas, is the source of the "blue-stones" of Stonehenge, supposed to have been carried to Salisbury Plain by Bronze Age man about 1500 years B.C. Recently, however, glacial deposits and erratics from West Wales have been discovered in Wiltshire and Somerset, and the theory of the human transport of the blue-stones is now open to doubt (Kellaway, 1971). An energetic, but probably inconclusive, debate on this topic between geologists and archaeologists can be guaranteed over the next few years!

The Silurian Outcrops

Silurian rocks are not particularly widespread in north Pembrokeshire, but where they do occur they seem to represent a similar type of marine deposition to that of Ordovician times. There are very few Silurian igneous rocks, but occasionally there are more beds of true sandstone and grit which assist in dating.

There are rocks supposed to be of Silurian age between Dinas Island and the Teifi Estuary in the north, but it is now thought that they may really be Ordovician. In the centre of the county a broad belt of Silurian "Llandovery" mudstones, sandstones and conglomerates runs from Haverfordwest (955155) to Narberth, with irregular outcrops also in the Wiston (022180) and Llawhaden areas (Fig. 4). Near Haverfordwest there are good exposures of the well-known "gasworks mudstones", which are rich in the fossils of brachiopods, corals and other marine creatures.

From the foregoing account it can be seen that an enormous variety of rock types can be examined in north Pembrokeshire, particularly in the exposures on the magnificent, wild coastline. With coastal scenery such as this to encourage them, little wonder that hordes of geologists over the last century or more have found excuses to examine the rocks of the coast in ever more minute detail!

SOUTHERN GEOLOGICAL PROVINCE

The geology of south Pembrokeshire is relatively simple, since most of the rocks are of sedimentary type, and only one small region has been affected by volcanic activity since Pre-Cambrian times. Except for a narrow band of ancient igneous rocks exposed between Talbenny (840120) and Benton, all of the rocks in this area were laid down on the southern edge of the Caledonian Mountains within the last 320 million years. The rocks are now exposed in a series of strips trending E.S.E.-W.N.W. (Fig. 9); these strips are the result of long-continued erosion which has exposed the rocks in the centres of the mountain ridges which were formed during the Armorican Orogeny (Fig. 1).

The most important structural feature which we should notice is the broad syncline which is filled with Coal Measures; this runs across the county from St Bride's Bay to Carmarthen Bay, and is

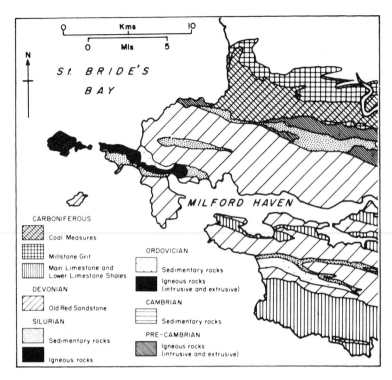

Figure 9: Simplified geological map of the "Southern Province" of Pembrokeshire.

simply the westernmost portion of the South Wales Coalfield. The Coal Measures are the youngest rocks in Pembrokeshire. On the flanks of the Coalfield there are strips of successively older rocks, but the "ideal" succession of rock types is disturbed by complicated faulting and folding; south of Milford Haven, for example, rock sequences are repeated several times as a result of alternating anticlines and synclines.

The oldest rocks of Pembrokeshire

By far the oldest rocks in the "southern province" are the Pre-

Cambrian igneous rocks exposed in an irregular belt between Talbenny and Benton (Fig. 5). The rocks exposed in parts of the cliffs north of Talbenny, and inland near Tier's Cross (906107), Johnston (935105) and Sardis, have been named by geologists the "Johnston Series". Mostly these rocks are diorites, but some of them have been altered by later igneous activity, and they are occasionally intruded by later (but still Pre-Cambrian) dykes. Probably the rocks of the Johnston Series are even older than the Pebidian volcanic rocks of north Pembrokeshire, i.e. well over 1,000 million years old. Another series of rocks in this same area, called the "Benton Series", are either Pre-Cambrian or (more probably) Silurian in age, and geologists are still trying to achieve a reliable dating.

Other Lower Palaeozoic rocks of south Pembrokeshire

Here and there in the south of the county there are narrow exposures of Ordovician sedimentary rocks along the eroded cores of anticlines. The centre of Freshwater East bay (020980), for example, is eroded in Ordovician rocks, with Silurian rocks exposed on either side (Fig. 9). The old village of Marloes is built on Ordovician rocks, which are exposed a short distance to the north-west in the cliffs at Musselwick Sands (785090). Silurian rocks are found more commonly; they may be discovered close to the outcrops of Pre-Cambrian rocks referred to in the paragraph above, and they occur also at the north end of the wide, wild Freshwater West Bay (880007) and in the smaller Lindsway Bay (845006) on Milford Haven. The most famous exposures of Silurian rocks, however, are those of Marloes Sands (785074) and the cliffs between Gateholm Island and Wooltack Point (755095). Here there is an almost complete sequence of the local Silurian rocks, for the most part exposed in steeply dipping (and occasionally almost vertical) beds along the magnificent cliffs. Much of the beauty of Marloes Sands is due to the jagged stacks of Silurian rocks which protrude through the sandy beach for some distance seawards of the cliffline. Among the rocks which may be examined here are basalts of the Skomer Volcanic Group (to the east of Mathew's Slade), various sandstones, conglomerates and ashes of approximately similar age (seen, for example, at Three Chimneys), and younger Silurian sedimentary rocks with plentiful fossils at either end of the bay. Where the footpath comes down to the beach the rocks belong to the "Coralliferous Series", and westward from this point the rocks become successively younger until the distinctive red colouring of the Old Red Sandstone can be seen on Gateholm. Faulting has disrupted the rocks exposed in the bay, and the full sequence is very complicated. Those who want to follow the sequence in detail are advised to look at Bassett's (1971) guide to the Marloes geological succession (pp. 213-217).

The volcanic rocks of Midland Isle and Skomer Island (725095) (including basalt, rhyolite and dolerite) have, for many years, been interpreted as Lower Ordovician in age. Indeed, they are shown on the Geological map (226/227) as belonging to the Arenig formation, and George (1970) supports this dating. However, other geologists have recently suggested that the Skomer Volcanic Group of rocks is of Silurian age, being closely linked with the sedimentary rocks of the Marloes area (Ziegler and others, 1969). Their arguments are convincing, and so the rocks of Skomer and the adjacent mainland are all shown as Silurian on Figure 9.

The Old Red Sandstone

At the end of Silurian times, about 400 million years ago, the great mountain-building phase of the Caledonian Orogeny led to the creation of the Caledonian Mountains (Fig. 1). North Pembrokeshire was located at the southern edge of these mountains, and during the 50 million years or so of the Old Red Sandstone period the southern parts of the mountains were largely worn away. Torrential streams flowed southwards, carrying loads of coarse detritus towards the coastline of the time, which ran

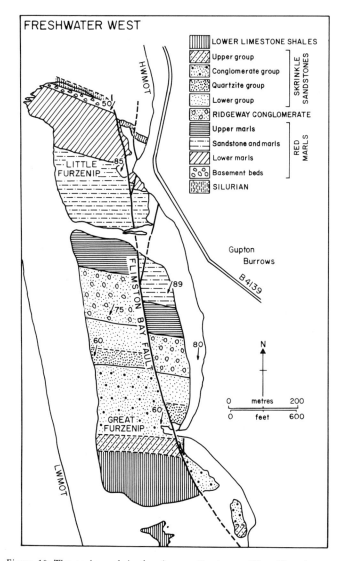

Figure 10: The geology of the foreshore at Freshwater West. Here, between L.W.M. and H.W.M., there is an excellent exposure of Old Red Sandstone rocks. Drawn from a map by Williams, 1971.

approximately east-west from the present Bristol Channel to southern Ireland. In south Pembrokeshire several thousands of feet of river and delta deposits were laid down, and these are now exposed over wide tracts of country particularly to the south of the Pembrokeshire Coalfield.

As the name suggests, the Old Red Sandstone rocks often have a distinctive red colour because of staining by iron oxide; but many strata have brown or green colourings also. The lowest formation of the Old Red Sandstone is the Red Marls, including several sedimentary "cycles" of conglomerate, sandstone and siltstone (Williams, 1971). The various rocks of the Red Marls can be seen clearly on the foreshore at Freshwater West (886990), where they have a total thickness of about 1,500 ft. (Fig. 10). The rocks are dipping steeply to the south, so they are exposed as a series of more or less parallel strips, parts of which are offset almost 400 ft. by the Flimston Bay fault. In many of the sandy beds there are traces of animal burrows, and fossils of molluscs, brachiopods and other animals can often be found. In addition to the excellent exposures at Freshwater West, the Red Marls occupy the spectacular cliffs described by Barrett (1966) around the Dale Peninsula (where they can be examined in Westdale Bay (799058) and on Great Castle Head), and for some distance on either side of Nab Head (790112). Much of the north shore of Milford Haven, from Lindsway Bay to Newton Noyes (920050), is made of Red Marls, and there are other excellent exposures on the south coast of the Castlemartin Peninsula around Greenala Point (008965) and between Freshwater East and Old Castle Head (076965). In Manorbier Bay (058975) these rocks can easily be examined, and because the strata are standing on edge one can see the way in which the hard sandstones and mudstones stand out as long ridges above the beds of softer shales and marls which have been more easily eroded.

Inland, the area where the Red Marls outcrop at the ground surface can be recognised by the bright red colour of soil in the fields. These red soils of south Pembrokeshire are sandy and warm, and

30

are famous today for their crops of early potatoes, particularly close to the coast.

Stratigraphically above the Red Marls are the Ridgeway Conglomerate and Skrinkle Sandstones, which vary greatly in thickness between one locality and another. The Ridgeway Conglomerate is dated to the middle part of the Old Red Sandstone period. It does not by any means consist only of conglomerate, but individual conglomerate beds are common, and sometimes they attain a thickness of 20 feet. Typical conglomerates can be seen at Freshwater West (Fig. 10), on the south side of Skrinkle Haven (080973) and on the north side of North Hill (865034) which separates the narrow Angle Valley from the waters of Milford Haven. The Skrinkle Sandstones are the youngest rocks of the Old Red Sandstone, and like the Ridgeway Conglomerates they are found only to the south of Milford Haven. As shown on Figure 5b, the Skrinkle Sandstones include conglomerates which occasionally contain pebbles of Pre-Cambrian rock. Among the sandstones there are also siltstones and white and buff quartzites, with the whole series passing upwards conformably to the Lower Limestone Shales. As the name suggests, this stratum provides a link with the overlying Carboniferous Limestone, and the contacts can be seen on the north side of West Angle Bay (852035), near Stackpole Quay (994959), and in Drinkim Bay (146963) on Caldey Island.

To the north and east of Milford Haven the Ridgeway Conglomerate and Skrinkle Sandstones are replaced by the Cosheston Beds, which are up to 10,000 feet thick and which are composed of greenish sandstones, marls, breccias and conglomerates. They are not very well exposed, but they occupy a broad area around Llanstadwell, Burton, Houghton, Upton and Cosheston (005037). The lower tidal reaches of the wide, wooded Daugleddau estuary are cut through the Cosheston Beds as far downstream as the old Neyland-Hobb's Point ferry (967047), and the Carew River (famous for its mud flats) has eroded its course along the contact between the Cosheston Beds and the Carboniferous Limestone (Fig. 9). It

31

is not commonly known that the famous Altar Stone at Stonehenge may have come from the Cosheston Beds (Kellaway, 1971).

Carboniferous Limestone

In the Upper Old Red Sandstone rocks of south Pembrokeshire the presence of occasional marine beds with salt-water fossils indicates the beginning of a general sinking of the land surface. The Lower Limestone Shales represent the start of this sinking and the change from land to submarine conditions about 345 million years ago, and the overlying Main Limestone represents the full development of conditions ideal for the growth of calcareous organisms in a clear, warm, shallow sea.

Today the Lower Limestone Shales and the Main Limestone are exposed in a number of irregular strips in synclines which follow the Armorican trend (Fig. 1). The Lower Limestone Shales consist of calcareous shales and thin limestones with a total thickness of 600 ft. They are well exposed, often in a rotten condition, in West Angle Bay. The largest exposures of the Main Limestone are in the south of the Castlemartin Peninsula, in the area unfortunately sat upon by the British Army. In the Middle Ages this was an area famous for barley crops, but now it is desolate and scarred with tank tracks. Here there is a magnificent stretch of coastline containing classic limestone cliff scenery, but access is so limited that the Flimston (926945) and St Govan's areas are the only ones which can be visited easily. Nevertheless, one can observe an enormous variety of coastal features (including stacks, caves and arches) around Flimston; in particular it is worth seeing the immense natural arch called the Green Bridge of Wales (Fig. 11), the towering Stack Rocks, and the complicated little peninsula enclosing the Devil's Cauldron (930946). Generally in this area the limestne beds are dipping northwards, and they are broken up by innumerable small fractures and many larger faults (Thomas, 1971); it is, however, difficult to examine the rocks in detail, and this can be done more easily on the sides of West Angle

Figure 11: The Green Bridge of Wales, a spectacular natural arch on the Carboniferous Limestone coast of the Castlemartin Peninsula. Note that the limestone beds are dipping inland at this point.

Bay, around Lydstep Point (094975), in Priory Bay (137968) on Caldey Island, and in the cliffs of Tenby's South Beach. In these localities the rocks are seen to contain many brachiopods, corals and other fossils, and occasionally these are so abundant that it seems that the whole rock mass is made of fossils. Geologists have classified the limestones not only on the basis of their lithology, but also on the combinations (or **assemblages**) of fossils contained.

Limestone has of course been a popular building stone throughout south Pembrokeshire, and there are many limestone quarries still to be seen. For example, one can visit the old limestone quarries at Lydstep Haven, Bosherston and Monkton, and many smaller quarries scar the landscape in isolated localities. Look for the characteristic grey-white fretted stone used in many walls and buildings in the limestone areas. Around West Williamston (035058) is one of the most impressive complexes of limestone quarries in the whole of South Wales; here many small quarries have been excavated below high water mark, and the limestone was exported on barges which entered the quarries via small channels or "docks". Much of the limestone from West Williamston was burnt in lime-kilns all around the Pembrokeshire coast, particularly in the last century when lime was an essential fertiliser.

Upper Carboniferous Rocks: Millstone Grit and Coal Measures

In the middle part of the Carboniferous period, perhaps 320 million years ago, conditions in south Pembrokeshire changed yet again, and the land surface was uplifted sufficiently to transform the shallow limestone seas into coastal deltas similar to those of the Old Red Sandstone period. There was great erosion on the exposed land surface, and eventually the rocks of the Millstone Grit and Coal Measures formations were laid down, particularly in the south of the county. These rocks are the youngest in Pembrokeshire; they must originally have covered a wide area, and were probably thousands of feet thick. However, erosion has subsequently removed them from the greater part of the county, and Upper Carboniferous rocks are now preserved only in the broad syncline of the Pembrokeshire Coalfield and in a narrow strip inland of Lydstep Haven (Fig. 9).

The Millstone Grit consists of conglomerates, gritstones, sandstones, shales and mudstones of many different types, attaining a total thickness of about 900 feet. There are even some thin layers of poor coal. There are exposures up to one mile wide along both the northern and southern edges of the coalfield, but the only easily accessible exposures are on the shore of Carmarthen Bay. The most magnificent sequence of Millstone Grit rocks can be seen just inside Carmarthenshire on the coastal section between Telpyn Point (185073) and Ragwen Point (220072), which can be walked from Amroth along the sands in about 3 ½ hours if care is taken with the tide. (Beware of the very large local tidal range, especially at the time of Spring Tides.) The sequence of rocks is

34

described in detail by Kelling and George, 1971. Other, less satisfactory, exposures of Millstone Grit can be seen (particularly by those who do not wish to stray too far from their comfortable hotels) along the Tenby North Beach Cliffs, although some sections of these cliffs are in too precarious a condition to be attacked by wild geologists armed with stout geological hammers.

The Coal Measures of Pembrokeshire, as noted earlier, are exposed in a broad belt stretching across the waist of the county. This belt widens eastward, but at the western end of the coalfield there is a detached section of Coal Measures around Nolton (858186) and Newgale (Fig. 4). Hence much of the coastline at the head of St Bride's Bay is made up of Coal Measures, which can be examined at leisure at Little Haven (856130), Broad Haven and the wide sweep of Newgale during pleasant strolls along the beach. Good exposures of the Coal Measures can also be examined around Picton Point (003117) (at the muddy yet beautiful confluence between the Western Cleddau and Eastern Cleddau), around Wiseman's Bridge, and at low tide between Saundersfoot Harbour and Monkstone Point. Most of the rocks in the coalfield basin are classified as Lower and Middle Coal Measures, and as in the western district of the South Wales Coalfield the coal beds themselves are largely of fine-quality anthracite (Edwards, 1963). The only rocks which are known to be Upper Coal Measures are some sediments bounded by faults in the Nolton-Newgale area. It is important to realise that coal itself makes up only a small proportion of the total thickness of the Coal Measures, and in Pembrokeshire coal mining operations have always suffered from the problems of exploiting thin, crumpled and shattered coal seams (Price, 1953). The Pembrokeshire Coalfield is more intensely deformed than any of the major coalfields of Britain, and some indications of this can be seen in folds such as the Sleekstone (Broad Haven), the Lady Cave Anticline at Saundersfoot, or the structures in the cliffs around Little Haven (Fig. 12). Little wonder that coal mining in Pembrokeshire was abandoned in 1948 at a time of rising costs and falling returns from anthracite

Figure 12: Some of the intense folds in Coal Measures, sandstones and shales near Little Haven. These deformations are typical of many parts of the Pembrokeshire Coalfield, and have been the cause of great problems in the working of coal seams.

sales. Now the coalfield is no longer of any economic importance, although there are innumerable traces within the landscape of the county's coal industry.

The soils which have developed on the Millstone Grit and Coal Measures are often wet and cold, and are not nearly so fertile as those of the Old Red Sandstone and Carboniferous Limestone areas. Note that many of the fields here are kept under lush grass for dairying and stock raising. Note also that in this area stone walls are not at all common, fields being bounded almost always by solid hedgerows or wire fences.

Since the deposition of the Pembrokeshire Coal Measures in an environment of semi-tropical swamps and a fluctuating sea-level, it is difficult to know what later rocks may have been laid down. The Armorican Orogeny, about 290 million years ago, had a great effect upon the structure of south Pembrokeshire, for it created the Armorican uplands which have gradually been denuded during Mesozoic and Tertiary times. There may have been Triassic and Cretaceous rocks in Pembrokeshire, and there is still a slight trace of Oligocene deposits in the south of the county; but overall the last 280 million years have witnessed far more erosion than deposition in this ancient south-western corner of Wales.

CONCLUSION

In this account of the rocks of Pembrokeshire I have tried to explain some of the fundamentals of geology. Also, I have tried to demonstrate how the local rocks have been formed and how they are distributed at the present time. There has been no space here to discuss the economic value of the Pembrokeshire rocks (slates for roofing, limestone for burning, sandstones for building, coal for heating), although the county has benefited for centuries from the great variety of strata exposed. There has been no space to describe in detail how the varied and attractive landscapes have evolved, particularly during the last 65 million years. And there has been no space to consider the events of the most recent geological period, the Quaternary Ice Age, which has seen the deposition of the unconsolidated deposits which may be the rocks of the future, and which has wrought fundamental changes in the geography of the county. These are tales still to be told.

APPENDIX I

SOME INTERESTING LOCALITIES

* Sites marked with an asterisk are geological "Sites of Special Scientific Interest". Please respect these localities and *do not* collect rock samples from them; many have already ben badly damaged by geologists, both professional and amateur.

* ABEREIDDY(797313) The bay is eroded into soft shales belonging to the Llandilo and Llanvirn formations of Ordovician age. There are excellent exposures in the quarries on the north side of the bay.

* BROAD HAVEN (North) (860140) This bay is cut entirely into Coal Measures. The headlands on the south side of the bay are made of Coal Measures sandstone, and to the north the famous Sleekstone is also a sandstone feature.

BROAD HAVEN (South) (978942) Carboniferous Limestone is exposed on both sides of the bay. There are limestone quarries just inland, and the bay is the outlet point for the stream from the popular Bosherston Pools.

* CAERBWDI (766244) In the bay, Cambrian rocks. Passing northwards up the valley the rocks become progressively older until Pre-Cambrian rocks are seen near Pont Clegyr.

* CAERFAI (760244) a famous locality for Cambrian rocks. From the Caerfai quarry on the clifftop came the purple sandstone used in the construction of St David's Cathedral. See Figure 8.

CARNINGLI (163373) The crag on the summit of Carningli Common is made of Ordovician instrusive rock, typical of many of the intrusions of the Preselau Hills.

CARNLLIDI (737280) This spectacular crag is formed of Ordovician dolerite, intruded into the sedimentary rocks which occupy the lower land all round.

CARN MEINI (143324) Dolerite, rhyolite and volcanic ash boulders are thought by archaeologists to have been transported by man to the famous stone circle at Stonehenge.

DALE PENINSULA (810050) Formed for the most part of the brightly-coloured Red Marls of the Old Red Sandstone.

* DRUIDSTON (860170) This attractive small bay (which is plugged with thick glacial deposits) is cut into Ordovician shales. The cliffs to the north are in Coal Measures, and those to the south are in Millstone Grit.

FLIMSTON (926945) In this area (a proposed National Nature Reserve) there is superb cliff scenery developed in Carboniferous Limestone. See Figure 11. Access is restricted by the Army during firing on the Castlemartin Range.

FRESHWATER EAST (020980) Silurian rocks and Old Red Sandstone are exposed on both sides of the bay.

* FRESHWATER WEST (880007) In the centre of the bay, many rocks of Old Red Sandstone age. Towards the north, Silurian rocks alsom See Figure 10.

JOHNSTON (935105) In this area may be found the "Johnston Series" of Pre-Cambrian rocks, thought to be the oldest in Pembrokeshire. See Figure 5.

LITTLE HAVEN (957130) The Haven itself is cut into soft Coal Measures shales, but the headlands are of sandstone. See Figure 12.

* MAIDEN CASTLE (954248) A spectacular crag (often likened to a "family of lions" by local people) made of Pre-Cambrian Roch Rhyolite. See Figure 6.

*MARLOES SANDS (785074) A beautiful bay with a comprehensive sequence of steeply-dipping Silurian rocks.

NEWGALE (847224) At the southern end of the long, sandy beach there are Coal Measures; at the northern end, good exposures of faulted Cambrian sedimentary rocks.

NOLTON HAVEN (858186) As at Little Haven, the bay is cut into soft Coal Measures shales, but the cliffs to the north are of sandstone. Old coal mines in the vicinity used the beach at Nolton for loading coastal vessels at low tide.

PICTON POINT (003117) Here there are low river cliffs with exposures of Coal Measures, including shales and ironstones.

*PORTH-CLAIS (743240) Between the road (at the head of the inlet) and the open coast there is a sequence of Pre-Cambrian and Cambrian rocks.

PORTHGAIN (807327) A fascinating small bay which was once the centre of a thriving quarrying and brick-making industry. Here there were quarries for Ordovician "slate" (behind the hoppers) and igneous rock (on the headland to the north-west).

ROCH CASTLE (880213) The crag on which the castle stands is of Pre-Cambrian Roch Rhyolite. See Figure 5.

ROSEBUSH SLATE QUARRIES (078300) From these large slate quarries (working Ordovician slates) have come the roofing slates for many Pembrokeshire buildings. Because of their attractive colouring the slates were used for the roofs of the Houses of Parliament.

ST GOVANS (967930) Apart from the famous chapel of St Govan, there is excellent Carboniferous Limestone cliff scenery in this vicinity.

*SAUNDERSFOOT (137045) All round Saundersfoot Bay the rock outcrops are of Coal Measures. Some coal may be seen in the cliffs, together with ironstones. Note the spectacular faults and folds south of the harbour.

SKOMER ISLAND (725095) A beautiful island formed entirely of rocks of the "Skomer Volcanic Group", now thought to be of Silurian age. A National Nature Reserve.

*SOLVA '800240) Solva Harbour has been eroded along a fault zone through Cambrian rocks of the Solva and Menevian Series. There are also Ordovician igneous rocks. Good exposures may be examined along the shore of the Gribin on the east side of the harbour.

*TENBY (133005) The cliffs of the South Beach, together with Castle Hill and St Catherine's Island, are of Carboniferous Limestone. The cliffs of North Beach are of Millstone Grit.

*TREFFGARNE GORGE (960245) A magnificent gorge of the Western Cleddau river, cut through Pre-Cambrian and Ordovician rocks

*WEST ANGLE BAY (852034) In the coves on the north side of the bay, excellent exposures of Carboniferous Limestonen Lower Limestone Shales and Old Red Sandstone.

WEST WILLIAMSTON (035050) Old limestone quarries, excavated largely during the time of limestone burning.

WHITESAND BAY (733270) A classic geological locality with sedimentary rocks of several Cambrian series. Also Pre-Cambrian rocks (at Ogofgolchfa) and Ordovician rocks (north of Trwynhwrddyn). See Figure 7.

A GLOSSARY OF SOME GEOLOGICAL TERMS

ACID ROCK: An igneous rock containing a large amount of silica. Granite is an acid igneous intrusive rock.

AGGLOMERATE: A mass of coarse rock fragments or blocks of lava produced by volcanic eruptions. Usually the fragments are angular.

ANDESITE: A volcanic rock occurring mainly as lava flows.

ANTHRACITE: A hard, shiny type of coal containing over 88 per cent of carbon. The Pembrokeshire Coalfield produced high-grade anthracite, at one time in great demand.

ANTICLINE: An arch or upfold in the rocks, generally produced by the bending upwards of the beds under pressure from the sides.

ARMORICAN OROGENY: The mountain-building episode at the end of Carboniferous and in early Permian times. From Armorica, that part of France now called Brittany.

ASH: The ejected fine material from a volcano.

ASSEMBLAGE: A number of animal species found together in fossil form. If the species actually lived together, they would be called a *community*.

BASAL LAYER: The lowest layer of a series of related strata.

BASALT: The commonest of all lavas; generally dark in colour and fine-grained.

BASIN: A depression in the earth's surface, usually filled by the deposition of sedimentary rocks.

BLUESTONE: The popular name for the foreign stone used in the construction of Stonehenge. Some of the bluestones are from the Carn Meini area of the Preselau Hills, but there are many different types.

BRACHIOPOD: Marine animal living in a calcareous shell composed of two more or less equal valves or parts joined together.

BRECCIA: A rock composed of broken, angular fragments of stone, generally cemented in a finer matrix.

CALEDONIAN OROGENY: The great mountain-building episode of late Silurian and early Devonian times. From Caledonia, or Scotland, where most mountains are of this age.

CAMBRIAN: The earliest geological period of the Palaeozoic, dated at 500-570 million years. Named after Cambria (Wales).

CARBONACEOUS SHALE: Shale containing a proportion of organic material, e.g. coal fragments.

CARBONIFEROUS: Literally "coal-bearing". This period lasted from 345 to 280 million years ago, and is classified as part of the Upper Palaeozoic era.

CENOZOIC: The "recent life" era, lasting from about 65 million years ago to the present. It includes the Tertiary and Quaternary periods.

CONGLOMERATE: A rock which consists of a mass of pebbles or rounded boulders set in a matrix of finer material.

CONFORMABLE CONTACT: Contact between adjacent beds which have been laid down in unbroken sequence one upon another.

CORAL: A hard stone of calcium carbonate, made of the skeletons of millions of small marine animals. Formed close to sea-level, often giving rise to a coral reef.

CRETACEOUS: The final period of the Mesozoic Era, ending about 65 million years ago. The chalk of southern England was laid down at this time.

CRUSTAL PLATE: A huge mass of the earth's solid crust which moves, more or less intact, across the mobile interior.

DENUDATION: The wearing down of the land by the processes of weathering and erosion.

DETRITUS: Rock waste produced during the wearing down of the earth's surface. Detritus can be subdivided as boulders, pebbles, gravel, sand, etc.

DEVONIAN: The geological period which followed the Caledonian Orogeny and lasted for about 50 million years. Named after the county of Devon, where rocks of this age are well exposed.

DIMETIAN: A group of intrusive igneous rocks of Pre-Cambrian age. Named after Dimetia, the Roman name for the South-west Peninsula of Wales.

DIORITE: A course-grained intrusive igneous rock. Often rather dark in colour.

DIP: The inclination of a bed of rock; measured in degrees from the horizontal.

DOLERITE: A dark-coloured igneous rock, resembling a basalt, but composed of larger crystals. Generally occurs in a dyke or a sill.

DYKE: A more or less vertical wall-like mass of igneous rock, which cuts across the rocks into which it is intruded.

EOZOIC: The earliest geological era, lasting from the creation of the earth until about 570 million years ago.

ERA: The longest unit of geological time. The Palaeozoic Era, for example, lasted for 345 million years.

EROSION: Wearing away of rocks at the earth's surface by natural agencies such as running water, glaciers, avalanches, wind, etc.

ERRATIC: A boulder or rock fragment transported some distance from its original bed, generally by the action of glacier ice.

EXTRUSIVE ROCK: Rock resulting from the solidification of lava at the ground surface.

FAULT: A dislocation in the rocks, where one side has moved relative to the other. Often visible as a fault-line.

FAUNA: The collective animal life of any given geological stratum.

FLAGSTONE: A rock with distinct, closely spaced bedding planes which allow it to break up into clean slabs or flags.

FOLD: A general term for any flexure or bend in the rocks caused by compression in the earth's crust.

FORMATION: Group of rocks which can be recognised as belonging to a certain geological period. For example, the Llandilo and Bala formations belonged to the Ordovician period.

FOSSIL: Anything found in a geological stratum which is recognisable as the remains of a plant or animal from a former period.

GABBRO: An intrusive igneous rock, usually coarse and crystalline.

GASTROPOD: Marine animal living in a single, usually coiled, calcareous shell.

GEOSYNCLINE: A very large trough-shaped depression on the earth's crust, often deepened as a prelude to the collision of adjacent continental plates.

GNEISS: A crystalline metamorphic rock, sometimes resembling granite but having a distinct banded appearance.

GRANITE: A coarse-grained igneous intrusive rock, often white or pink in colour.

GRAPTOLITE: Extinct marine animal (frequently found in Ordovician and Silurian rocks) with a simple, branching skeleton.

GRIT: A coarse type of sandstone, composed of large and sometimes angular grains of quartz.

41

GREYWACKE: A dark-coloured grit or coarse sandstone, made from muddy marine sands.

HERCYNIAN OROGENY: Named after the Harz Mountains in Germany. This an alternative name for the Armorican Orogeny. Some writers use the term 'Variscan'.

HORIZON: A stratum or set of strata characterised by a particular set of fossils.

IGNEOUS ROCK: A rock formed by the solidification of molten material from the earth's interior.

INTRUSIVE ROCK: A rock which has been forced, while in a molten state, into the cavities or cracks in pre-exisiting rock strata.

JOINT: A line of breakage which cuts across a rock stratum and allows its separation into blocks. Most joints are due to shrinkage or contraction during the consolidation of the rock.

LAVA: Molten igneous rock which has flowed from the earth's interior (often during a volcanic eruption) to cool and solidify at the surface.

LIMESTONE: A rock consisting mainly of calcium carbonate. There are many types of limestone, but most are of organic origin, consisting of the hard parts of organisms such as seashells or corals. The rock can be dissolved by ground-water or rainwater containing carbon dioxide.

LITHOLOGY: The physical character of a rock, described in terms of its mineral content, structure, grain-size, and the arrangement of its constituent parts.

MARBLE: Limestone which has been altered to a hard crystalline state by metamorphic processes.

MARL: A rock made of clay and calcium carbonate, usually laid down in water.

MESOZOIC: The "middle life" era, lasting from approximately 225 million to 65 million years ago. It was preceded by the Palaeozoic Era and followed by the Cenozoic Era.

METAMORPHIC ROCK: Rock which has been changed so much by heat or pressure that it deserves to be classed as a separate rock type.

MINERAL: A solid inorganic substance which has recognisable physical and chemical properties. Rocks are usually mixtures of minerals. While there are well over 2,000 minerals, only about 10 are common in most rocks.

MINERALOGY: The science of the study of minerals found in rocks.

MOLLUSC: An animal belonging to the very large "Phylum Mollusca", which includes snails, slugs, clams, oysters, squids and the octopus. Small marine molluscs may live in either single or double shells.

MUDSTONE: A fine-grained sedimentary rock, usually formed of silt and clay laid down in deep water.

OLIGOCENE: One of the periods of the Tertiary which lasted from about 40 million to about 25 million years ago. May be loosely translated as "slightly recent".

ORDOVICIAN: A period of the Lower Palaeozoic Era which lasted from about 500 million years ago to 440 million years ago. Named after the Ordovices, a large pre-Roman tribe in north-central Wales.

ORGANIC MATERIAL: Material originating in plants or animals.

OROGENY: One of the great mountain-building periods, probably caused by a collision between two or more of the earth's crustal plates.

OUTCROP: That part of a rock stratum which is visible at the land surface.

PALAEONTOLOGY: The study of fossil animals found in rocks.

PALAEOBOTANY: The study of fossil plants found in rocks.

PALAEOGEOGRAPHY: The study of the physical geography of former geological periods, interpreted from the nature and distribution of rock types.

PALAEOZOIC: The "ancient life" era, lasting from about 570 million years ago to 225 million years ago.

PEBIDIAN: A group of volcanic rocks of Pre-Cambrian age. Named after Pebidiog, the medieval name for St David's Peninsula.

PERIOD: One of the main units of geological time. Each era is divided into a number of periods.

PETROLOGY: The study of rocks, including the systematic description of rocks and the study of their origins.

PILLOW-LAVA: Lava laid down in the sea, so that is has the appearance of pillows piled one on top of another.

PRE-CAMBRIAN: The immensely long geological period lasting from the birth of the earth (about 5,000 million years ago) until 570 million years ago. Note that this period was very much longer than the rest of more recent geological time put together.

PRIMARY: The Primary Era (badly named, since it was not the first at all) is the same as the Palaeozoic Era.

QUATERNARY: The Quaternary (Fourth) System has occupied the last 2 million years, and is still with us. Commonly termed the "Ice Age". Part of the Cenozoic Era.

RAB: A local term for the soft shales of various Ordovician formations which are widespread in north Pembrokeshire. These shales break up easily into sharp-edged stones and flakes when weathered.

RHYOLITE: A fine-grained grey or white acid lava, the volcanic equivalent of granite.

SANDSTONE: A sedimentary rock composed mainly of quartz grains, and representing a compacted bed of sand.

SEDIMENTARY ROCK: Rock composed of organic or inorganic sediments, directly laid down after erosion and transport by the agents of denudation.

SHALE: A fine-grained sedimentary rock formed mainly from particles of clay and silt. It may be finely stratified.

SILL: A sheet of igneous rock, formed from the solidification of magma which has been intruded between layers of rock. Sills may be near horizontal in flat-lying bedrock, but in Pembrokeshire they are usually tilted.

SILTSTONE: A rock formed of silt particles cemented together. It is much smoother to the touch than a sandstone.

SILURIAN: One of the periods of the Lower Palaeozoic Era. Named after the Silures, a tribe which lived in south-east Wales in pre-Roman times.

SLATE: A dense, fine-grained metamorphic roch which readily splits into thin, smooth plates suitable for roofing purposes.

STRATIGRAPHY: The study of the succession through time of the various rock formations. Sometimes called Historical Geology

STRATUM: A distinct layer or bed of rock which can usually be traced for some distance. Usually, but not always, of sedimentary rock. Plural: strata.

STRIKE: A horizontal line drawn along a rock layer perpendicular to the direction of dip.

STRUCTURE: The disposition or arrangement of rock masses following some disturbance by earth movements.

SYNCLINE: A trough or downwarp in the rocks, usually produced as a result of the buckling of strata on its flanks.

TERTIARY: The "third life" period lasting from 65 million years ago to 2 million years ago. The Tertiary should strictly be considered, along with the Quaternary, as part of the Cenozoic Era.

TEXTURE: The physical appearance of a rock's internal structure.

TREND: Orientation of the main structural lines (e.g. lines of folding and faulting) in a region.

TRIASSIC: The earliest period of the Mesozoic Era, so named because the Triassic rocks have a three-fold division in Germany.

TRILOBITE: Extinct class of marine crustaceans which dominated the organic world during the Cambrian but which declined gradually thereafter. Became extinct during the Permian Period.

TUFF: A rock composed of fine-grained material (often ash) ejected by volcanoes. It may be arranged in beds or layers which have accumulated under water.

UNCONFORMITY: A contact along which a younger group of rocks rests upon the eroded surface of an older group of rocks. Often the beds of the older group of rocks are truncated at the unconformity.

UNIFORMITARIANISM: The theory (established in particular by Charles Lyell) that all changes in and on the earth's crust are due to the fairly uniform action of the forces now at work.

WEATHERING: The breaking down of rock surfaces as a result of exposure to rain, wind, frost, temperature changes, groundwater, etc.

For terms not included in the above glossary, many more definitions of technical terms can be found in the following texts:

American Geological Institute, 1962 *"Dictionary of Geological Terms"*, Dolphin Books, 545 pp.

Challinor, J. 1967 *"The Dictionary of Geology"* (3rd ed.), Cardiff, 298 pp.

Fairbridge, R. W. 1969 *"The Encyclopedia of Geomorphology"*, Van Nostrand, 1,295 pp.

Jones, W. R. and Williams, D. 1954 *"Minerals and Mineral Deposits"*, O.U.P., 248 pp.

Monkhouse, F. J. 1970 *"A Dictionary of Geography"*, Arnold, London, 384 pp.

Moore, D. G. 1962 *"A Dictionary of Geography"*, Penguin.

Open University, 1971 *"Major Features of the Earth's surface"*, Science Foundation Course Units 24 and 25.

Open University 1971 *"Earth History I and II"*, Science Foundation Course Units 26 and 27.

Open University 1972 *"Surface Processes"*, S23-Block 5.

Putnam, W. C. 1971 *"Geology"* (2nd editionn revised), O.U.P., 586 pp.

Stamp, L. D. (ed.) 1961 *"A glossary of geographical terms"*, Longmans, London, 539 pp.

Trueman, A. E. 1972 *"Geology and Scenery in England and Wales"*, Penguin (new edition, revised by Whittow, J. B. and Hardy, J. R.), 400 pp.

LIST OF REFERENCES

General Texts

Bennison, G. M. and Wright, A. E. 1969 *"The Geological History of the British Isles"*, Arnold, London, 406 pp.

Bloom, A. L. 1969 *"The Surface of the Earth"*, Prentice-Hall, U.S.A.

† Cailleux, A. 1968 *"Anatomy of the Earth"*, Weidenfeld & Nicholson, London, 255 pp.

† Calder, N. 1972 *"Restless Earth"* BBC, London, 152 pp.

Dury, G. H. 1959 *"The Face of the Earths ', Pelican 223 pp.

Eicher, D. L. 1968 "Geologic Time", Prentice-Hall, U.S.A.

† Evans, I. O. 1971 *"The Observer s Book of Geology"*, Open University, 355 pp.

Holmes, A. 1965 *"Principles of Physical Geology"*, Nelson, London.

† Kirkaldy, J. F. 1971 *"General Principles of Geology"*, Hutchinsons, (5th ed.).

† Kirkaldy, J. F. 1970 *"Fossils in Colour"*, Blandford.

† Kirkaldy, J. F. 1968 *"Minerals and Rocks in Colour"* (2nd ed.), Blandford, 184 pp.

Kummel, B. 1970 *"History of the Earth"*, Freeman, U.S.A., 707 pp.

Longwell, C. R. and others, 1969 *"Physical Geology"*, John Wiley, U.S.A.

Mears, B. 1970 *"The Changing Earth"*, London, 425 pp.

† Middlemiss, F. A. 1969 *"British Stratigraphy"*, George Allen & Unwin, 48 pp.

Oakley, K. P. and Muir-Wood, H. M. 1967 *"The Succession of Life through Geological time"*, Brit. Museum, 96 pp.

Rankilor, P. R. 1972 *"British Palaeography"*, John Sherratt.

Rayner, D. H. 1967 *"The Stratigraphy of the British Isles"*, London, 453 pp.

Read, H. H. 1968/1973 *"Introduction to Geology"* (2 vols.), Macmillan.

† Read, H. H. 1970 *"Beginning Geology"*, London, 246 pp.

† Robinson, H. 1969 *"Morphology and Landscape"*, U.T.P., 392 pp.

Small, R. J. 1970 *"The Study of Landforms"*, Cambridge U.P., 486pp.

Sparks, B. W. 1971 *"Rocks and Relief"*, Longman, London, 404 pp.

† Stamp, L. D. 1955 *"Britain's Structure and Scenery"*, Collins, London, 255 pp.

Steers, J. A. 1960 *"The Coast of England and Wales in pictures"*, Cambridge.

Steers, J. A. 1964 *"The Coastline of England and Wales"*, Cambridge, 749 pp.

Swinnerton, H. H. *"Fossils"*, Collins, London.

Tarling, D. H. and M. P. 1971 *"Continental Drift"*, Bell, London, 112 pp.

† Watts, W. W. 1959 *"Geology for Beginners"*, Macmillan, London, 366 pp.

Williams, H. and James H. P. 1972 *"The Physical Basis of the British Isles"*, Macmillan, London.

Wills, L. 1968 *"Palaeogeographical Atlas"*, London, 64 pp.

Wilson, J. T. (ed.) 1972 *"Continents Adrift"* (Readings from Scientific American), Freeman, U.S.A. 172 pp.

Zim, H. S. and Schaffer, P. R. 1965 *"Rocks and Minerals"*, Paul Hamlyn.

South Wales Geology

Bassett, D. A. and Bassett, M. G. (eds.) 1971 *"Geological Excursions in South Wales and the Forest of Dean"*, Cardiff, 267 pp.

Brown, E. H. 1960 *"The Relief and Drainage of Wales"*, Cardiff.

† Evans, D. E. 1971 *"Welsh Scenery"*, Nat. Museum of Wales, 36 pp.

George, T. N. 1970 *"South Wales"* (British Regional Geology, 3rd ed.), H.M.S.O., 152 pp.

Bassett, D. A. 1968 "Directory of British geology. 1, a provisional annotated bibliography and index of geological excursion guides and reports for areas in Britain. (B) Wales and the Welsh borders", *Welsh geol. Quarterly* 3 (1), 3-23.

† Howe, G. M. 1957 *"Wales from the Air"*, Cardiff, 42 pp.

North, F. J. 1964 *"The Evolution of the Bristol Channel"*, Cardiff (3rd ed.), 110 pp.

† Owen, T. R. 1973 *"Geology Explained in South Wales"*, David & Charles.

Owen, T. R. & Rhodes, F. H. T. 1960 *"Geology around the University towns: Swansea, South Wales"*, Geologist's Association Guide No. 17, 20 pp.

Owen, T. R. and others, 1965 "Summer (1964) field meeting in South Wales", *Proc. Geol. Ass.* 76, 463-95.

Wood, A. (ed.) 1969 *"The Pre-Cambrian and Lower Palaeozoic rocks of Wales"*, Cardiff, 461 pp.

Yates, R. A. 1957 *"Physiographic Evolution"*, Ch. 1 in Bowen, E. G. (ed.), *"Wales"*, Methuen, London, pp. 19-52.

Pembrokeshire Geology

Baker, J. W. 1971 "The Pre-Cambrian rocks of Pembrokeshire", Ch. 15 in Bassett & Bassett (eds), 170-179.

† Barrett, J. H. 1966 *"A Plain Man's Guide to the path round the Dale Peninsula"*, Haverfordwest, 40 pp.

† Barrett, J. H. 1970 "Some outline notes to acompany the geology map of Pembrokeshire", Pembs. Coast Nat. Park leaflet.

Bassett, M. G. 1971 'Silurian rocks of the south Pembrokeshire coast ', Ch. 18 in Bassett & Bassett (eds), 206-221.

Bloxam, T. W. 1971 "Haverfordwest, Strumble Head and Abereiddy Bay", Ch. 17 in Bassett & Bassett (eds), 199-205.

Cantrill, T. C. and others 1916. The geology of the South Wales coalfield, Part 12. The country around Milford. *Mem. geol. Surv. U.K.*, 185 pp.

Cox, A. H. and others, 1930 "The geology of the St David's district, Pembrokeshire", *Proc. Geol. Ass.*, 41, 241-73.

† Davies, M. F. 1939 *"Pembrokeshire"*, Part 32 of L. D. Stamp (ed.), *The Land of Britain,* Report Land Utilization Survey, London, pp. 75-170.

Dixon, E. E. L. 1921. The geology of the South Wales Coalfield, Part 13. The country around Pembroke and Tenby. *Mem. geol. Surv. U.K.* 220 pp.

Edwards, G. 1963 "The Coal Industry in Pembrokeshire", Field Studies 1 (5), 1-32.

† Evans, R. O. and John B. S. 1973 *"The Pembrokeshire Landscape"*, Five Arches Press, Tenby, 120 pp.

† John, B. S. 1972 *"The Fishguard and Pembroke Area"* (British Landscapes through Maps, No. 16). Geog. Assoc., 35 pp.

Kellaway, G. A. 1971 'Glaciation and the stones of Stonehenge' , *Nature, London,* 232 (5314), 30-35.

Kelling, G. & George G. T. 1971 "Upper Carboniferous sedimentation in the Pembrokeshire Coalfield", Ch. 20 in Bassett & Bassett (eds), 240-259.

Owen, T. R. and others, 1971. "Summer (1968) field meeting in Pembrokeshire, South Wales", *Proc. Geol. Ass.* 82, 17-60.

† Price, J. A. (ed.) 1963 *"Pembroke County Development Plan"*, Ch. IV, Geology; and Ch. X, Minerals.

Stead, J. T. G. and Williams, B. P. 1971 "The Cambrian rocks of north Pembrokeshire", Ch. 16 in Bassett & Bassett (eds), 180-198.

Strahan, A. and others, 1914 The Geology of the South Wales coalfield, Pt. 11. The country around Haverfordwest. *Mem. geol. Surv. U.K.*, 262 pp.

Thomas, T. M. 1970 "Field meeting of the South Wales Group on the Stack Rocks to Bullslaughter Bay section of the south Pembrokeshire coast". *Proc. Geol. Ass.*, 81, 241-48.

Williams, B. P. 1971 "Sedimentary features of the Old Red Sandstone and Lower Limestone Shales of South Pembrokeshire, south of the Ritec Fault", Ch. 19 in Bassett & Bassett (eds), 222-239.

Williams, T. G. 1934 The Pre-Cambrian and Lower Palaeozoic rocks of the eastern end of the St David's Pre-Cambrian area, *Q. Jl geol. Soc. Lond.*, 90, 32-75.

Ziegler, A. M. and others, 1969 Correlation and environmental setting of the Skomer Volcanic Group, Pembrokeshire, *Proc. Geol. Ass.*, 80, 409-39.

NOTES

* This list is not by any means exhaustive; the reader should consult the standard texts for further references, and especially Bassett & Bassett (eds), 1971.

† Reading especially useful for those with no previous knowledge of geology.

© 1979 Dr Brian S. John

Reprinted 1993, 1996, 2000

Published by
Abercastle Publications
Blaenrhos, Lady Road, Blaenporth
Aberteifi/Cardigan, Ceredigion SA43 2BG
Tel: 01239 811267

Printed by Dinefwr Press, Llandybie, Carms.